WRESTLEMANIA XXIV

KANE VS CHAVO

EDGE VS UNDERTAKER!!!

£7.99

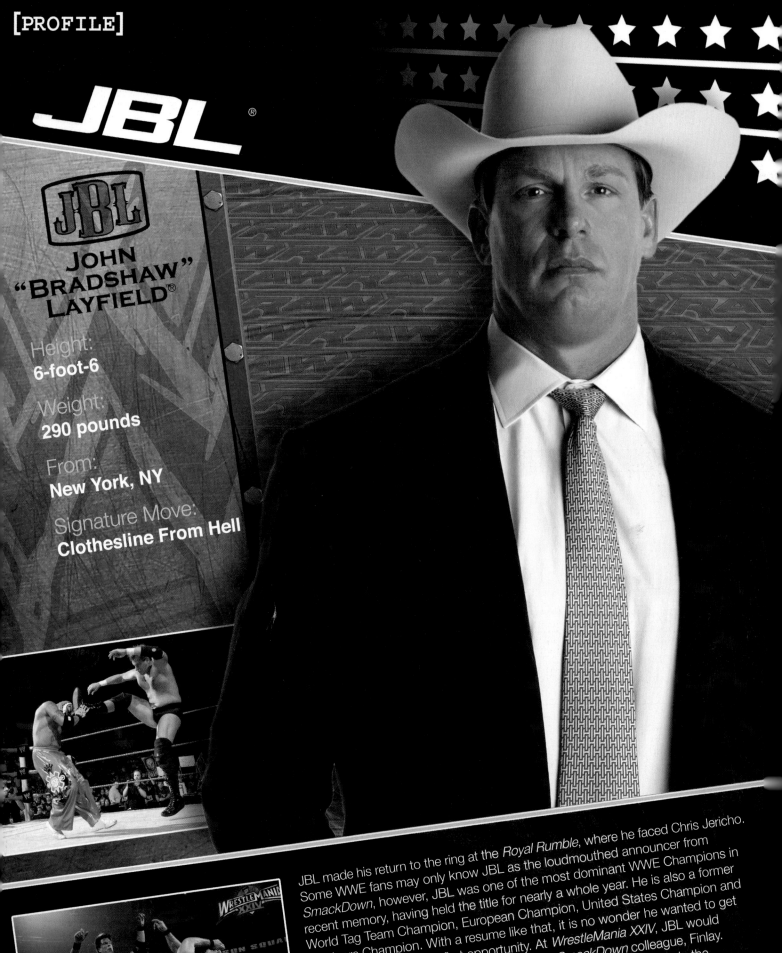

JBL ®

JOHN "BRADSHAW" LAYFIELD ®

Height:
6-foot-6

Weight:
290 pounds

From:
New York, NY

Signature Move:
Clothesline From Hell

JBL made his return to the ring at the *Royal Rumble*, where he faced Chris Jericho. Some WWE fans may only know JBL as the loudmouthed announcer from *SmackDown*, however, JBL was one of the most dominant WWE Champions in recent memory, having held the title for nearly a whole year. He is also a former World Tag Team Champion, European Champion, United States Champion and Hardcore Champion. With a resume like that, it is no wonder he wanted to get back into the ring at the first opportunity. At *WrestleMania XXIV*, JBL would face a man he knows all too well, his former *SmackDown* colleague, Finlay. JBL must have called hundreds of the fighting Irishman's matches in the past and you can bet he will use that knowledge to gain an advantage over his opponent.

FINLAY & HORNSWOGGLE™

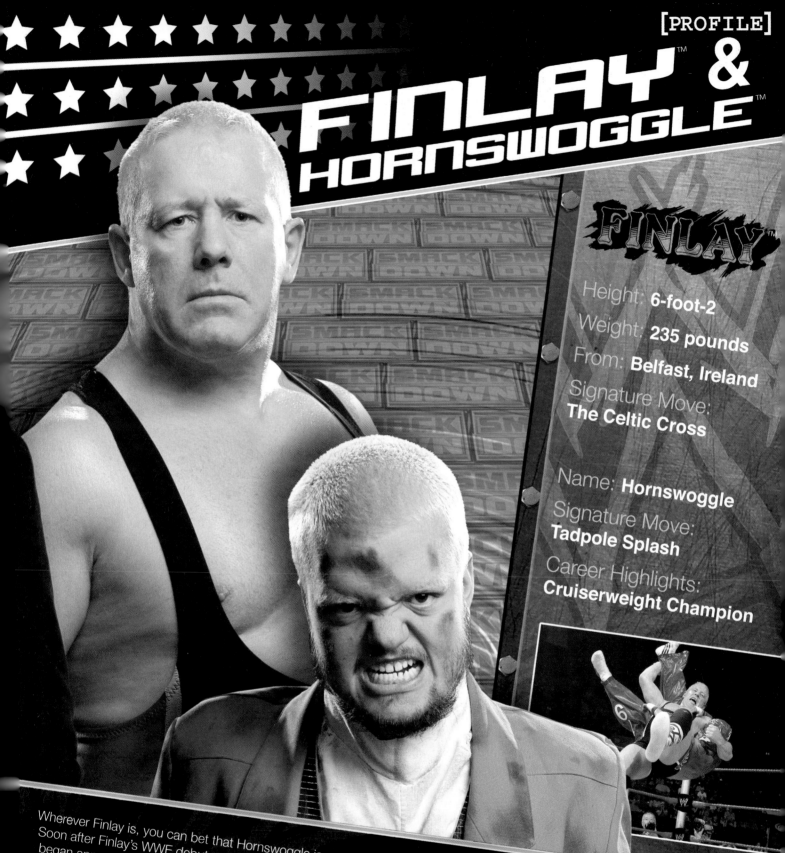

FINLAY™

Height: **6-foot-2**

Weight: **235 pounds**

From: **Belfast, Ireland**

Signature Move:
The Celtic Cross

Name: **Hornswoggle**

Signature Move:
Tadpole Splash

Career Highlights:
Cruiserweight Champion

Wherever Finlay is, you can bet that Hornswoggle is somewhere close behind. Soon after Finlay's WWE debut, a strange mini-version of the fighting Irishman began appearing during his matches. In 2007, Hornswoggle was revealed as the illegitimate son of WWE Chairman Mr McMahon. JBL, however, made the revelation that Hornswoggle was not a McMahon at all and was, in fact, Finlay's son! The beloved leprechaun was taking on the man he believed to be his father, Mr McMahon, in a steel cage match when JBL brutally attacked Hornswoggle and hospitalized him. This infuriated Finlay, and soon afterward, a *Belfast Brawl Match* was signed for *WrestleMania XXIV*. Could Finlay and Hornswoggle overcome JBL, or would the father and son become just another two Superstars to be defeated by the 'Wrestling God'?

JBL JOHN "BRADSHAW" LAYFIELD® Vs FINLAY

"Here comes the 'Wrestling God', JBL! This is going to be a brutal match!"

"JBL looks ready for this Belfast Brawl. Anything goes here tonight at *WrestleMania XXIV!*"

"And here is Finlay! And look, he has Hornswoggle with him!"

"Finlay sure is the favourite in this match. Just listen to the crowd's reaction!"

"JBL is wasting no time here! He's going to work on Finlay with that trash can!"

"JBL is just plain vicious! This match may not last long!"

"Look at poor Hornswoggle looking on as his father is being battered by JBL!"

"JBL has the steel ring steps in the ring, and I think he is trying to piledrive Finlay! Finlay counters and delivers a backdrop to the former WWE Champion!"

"Finlay with a steel chair! That really rung JBL's bell!"

"Finlay looks like he is in complete control of the match now! What an incredible kick to the side of the head!"

"Finlay has the trash can lid! And he delivers a huge shot to the head!"

"And another shot to the head! I don't know how JBL is still standing."

"JBL is down, and Finlay has placed the trashcan over his face! Finlay just stomped the trashcan into JBL's skull!"

"But JBL is back to his feet hits Finlay with several lefts and rights, which sends the Irishman reeling."

"JBL is back in control but... look at this, Hornswoggle just hit JBL with a cane! JBL hardly felt it, and now he is attacking Hornswoggle!"

"Finlay makes the save and drives JBL face first into the floor on the outside!"

"Finlay is going for that face stomp again!"

"But somehow JBL escaped and is back on the offensive."

"JBL is going after Hornswoggle again, and this time Finlay is not around to save him."

"JBL almost took the little guy's head off with that punch!"

"Finlay slams JBL's head into the announcers table! Wow! That can't feel good."

"Finally, Finlay makes the save and rescues his son!"

"Both men are back in the ring, and Finlay delivers another shot to JBL's cranium!"

"Finlay just hit the Celtic Cross. This one should be over!"

"Finlay has set up a table in the corner of the ring!"

"And he sends JBL crashing straight through it!"

"I am sure the whole ring just moved! What an impact!"

"Finlay has the steel steps. He is going to slam them onto JBL!"

"JBL catches Finlay with a low blow and escapes! Look at that! Clothesline From Hell!"

"JBL is going for the pin. 1...2...3! It's all over! JBL has won it!"

"What a brutal match. I am sure both men are glad that it is over!"

"JBL is victorious in the opening match at *WrestleMania XXIV!*"

"As JBL makes his way up the ramp, Hornswoggle comes into the ring to check on his father!"

"I don't think we have seen the end of this rivalry yet. Finlay will be looking for revenge after that loss."

WRESTLEMANIA QUIZ

Q1. In an untelevised match before *WrestleMania XXIV*, how many other Superstars did Kane defeat in a battle royal to earn a shot at the ECW Championship later that evening?

A. 29
B. 24
C. 23

Q2. What move did JBL use to defeat Finlay in the *Belfast Brawl Match*?

A. Clothesline From Hell
B. Powerbomb
C. Figure Four Leglock

Q3. Who defeated JBL at *WrestleMania 21* to end his historic run as WWE Champion?

A. Triple H
B. John Cena
C. Rey Mysterio

Q4. Who defeated JBL and forced him into retirement in May 2006?

A. John Cena
B. Rey Mysterio
C. Tazz

Q5. What is the only WWE title Finlay has held?

A. United States Championship
B. Hardcore Championship
C. Intercontinental Championship

WELCOME TO THE FIRST PART OF THE *WRESTLEMANIA* QUIZ...

In this quiz, you will find tons of questions about WWE's biggest event of the year and all the Superstars that took part in it!

So do you think you have what it takes to call yourself a WWE expert? Do you know everything about Beth Phoenix to Undertaker? This is the place to find out!

Q6. At which *WrestleMania* did the *Money In The Bank Ladder Match* debut?

A. *WrestleMania XX*
B. *WrestleMania 21*
C. *WrestleMania X-7*

Q7. Who was the winner of the first *Money In The Bank Ladder Match?*

A. Edge
B. Rob Van Dam
C. Jeff Hardy

Q8. Who did CM Punk defeat to qualify for the *Money In The Bank Ladder Match* at *WrestleMania XXIV?*

A. Matt Striker
B. Tommy Dreamer
C. Big Daddy V

Q9. Who did Edge defeat for the WWE Championship after cashing in his *Money In The Bank Ladder Match* contract at *New Year's Revolution 2006?*

A. Undertaker
B. John Cena
C. Rob Van Dam

Q10. Who is the only winner of a *Money In The Bank Ladder Match* contract to have never cashed it in against a World Champion?

A. Shelton Benjamin
B. Mr Kennedy
C. Edge

SHELTON BEJAMIN®

Shelton **BENJAMIN**®

Height:
6-foot-2

Weight:
245 pounds

From:
Orangeburg, SC

Signature Move:
T-bone Suplex

Growing up in an especially tough part of Orangeburg, SC, Shelton Benjamin had only two choices — become involved with gangs or focus on athletics. An exceptional athlete, Shelton won two South Carolina state high school amateur wrestling championships. He was accepted to the University of Minnesota, continuing his career as a standout amateur wrestler and eventually becoming a WWE Superstar. After becoming a multi-time WWE Tag Team Champion with his then-partner, Charlie Haas, Benjamin entered the singles division and quickly captured the Intercontinental Championship. In November 2007, Benjamin became an *ECW* Superstar. He has since tagged himself the 'Gold Standard' of *ECW*, in his efforts to become the next *ECW* Champion. Winning the *Money In The Bank Ladder Match* at WrestleMania XXIV would take him one step closer to his goal.

CM PUNK

Height:
6-foot-1

Weight:
222 pounds

From:
Chicago, IL

Signature Move:
G.T.S. (Go to Sleep);
Anaconda Vise

Since CM Punk debuted in WWE in 2006, he has become one of the most popular Superstars in the company. He has also proven himself to be a top Superstar. In 2007, he defeated John Morrison for the *ECW* Championship and earned himself a place in WWE history. A man who was once described as 'the future of WWE' by Triple H, CM Punk is on his way to the top. He earned his chance to compete in *The Money In The Bank Ladder Match* at *WrestleMania XXIV* by defeating the massive Big Daddy V. Growing up, CM Punk idolized such WWE Legends as 'Rowdy' Roddy Piper and Jimmy 'Superfly' Snuka. Now he has the chance to perform on the biggest stage WWE has to offer in one of the most exciting matches in WWE history. Will Punk be able to use his skills in one of WWE's most brutal matches and climb the ladder to success, only time will tell.

CHRIS JERICHO

Height:
6 foot

Weight:
231 pounds

From:
Manhasset, N.Y.

Signature Move:
Codebreaker; Walls of Jericho; Lionsault

Chris Jericho made his WWE debut in 1999. After a successful career in Canada, Mexico, Japan and WCW, the 'Ayatollah of Rock 'n' Rolla' immediately became a main-event Superstar on both *Raw* and *SmackDown*. Jericho cemented his place in WWE history on December 9, 2001 at *Vengeance*, when he beat both The Rock for the WCW Championship and 'Stone Cold' Steve Austin for the WWE Championship to unify both titles and become the first Undisputed WWE Champion. Since returning to WWE in 2007, Jericho has once again proven his worth taking on some of the greatest Superstars on the WWE roster.

18

CARLITO

Height:
5-foot-10

Weight:
220 pounds

From:
The Caribbean

Signature Move:
Back Stabber

Carlito, son of the great Puerto Rican star Carlos Colon, made his WWE debut on *SmackDown* in October 2004. He shocked the world when, in his very first WWE match, he defeated John Cena for the United States Championship. Other WWE Superstars could not fail to take notice of this cocky new talent who likes to 'spit in the face of people who don't want to be cool!' Carlito shocked the world again when in 2005, he was drafted to *Raw* and once again made an incredible debut, this time defeating Shelton Benjamin for the Intercontinental Championship, a title he would hold until he lost to Ric Flair later that year. Carlito defeated Cody Rhodes on *Raw* to qualify for his first *Money In The Bank Ladder Match* at *WrestleMania XXIV*, and you can bet that he has every intention of taking the contract for himself. That would be cool!

MVP™

MVP

Height:
6-foot-3

Weight:
252 pounds

From:
Miami, FL

Signature Move:
Playmaker

MVP was originally brought to *SmackDown* by then-general manager Theodore Long. Signing MVP was not easy. MVP was hyped by his agents as 'the most talented free agent in the game', and he was in high demand from organizations all over the world. Despite Long's requests, MVP made it clear that he wasn't getting in the ring until a contract was signed, because as MVP's saying goes, 'no contract, no contact'. Since his debut, MVP has proved that the hype was justified, as he defeated Superstars such as Batista and Ric Flair. After MVP won the United States Championship at *Judgment Day 2007*, he went on to become the most dominant United States Champion in WWE history, holding the title for 343 days.

MR KENNEDY™

MR. KENNEDY™

Height:
6-foot-2

Weight:
243 pounds

From:
Green Bay, WI

Signature Move:
The Mic Check

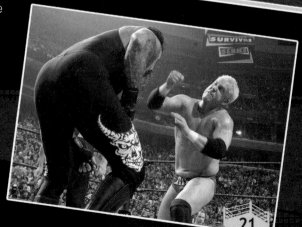

Give the bodacious loudmouth Mr Kennedy credit: He sure knows how to make an entrance. And he sure won't let anyone outtalk him – ask any poor soul who has been on the receiving end of a verbal drubbing by him. After winning the *Money in The Bank Ladder Match* at *WrestleMania 23* only to lose the contract in a match against Edge a few weeks later, Kennedy was incredibly focused on becoming the first two time winner at *WrestleMania XXIV*. After destroying Val Venis in his qualifier on *Raw*, many people considered Kennedy to be the favourite going into the match. So what fuels Mr Kennedy's desire? Maybe it is his huge ego. Maybe it's greed. One thing is for sure. After the events of the previous year, Mr Kennedy will want to win this match more than any other Superstar.

JOHN MORRISON™

John Morrison

Height:
6-foot-1

Weight:
219 pounds

From:
Los Angeles, CA

Signature Move:
Snapshot;
Moonlight Drive

John Morrison endured a personal evolution of sorts after capturing the vacated *ECW* Championship at *Vengeance: Night of Champions* in 2007. Formerly known as Johnny Nitro, he officially renamed himself John Morrison, his given birth name. Morrison had reached the peak of his fame with the *ECW* Championship and he believed he could 'be himself' from that point forward. Shortly thereafter, Morrison found unexpected success alongside another brazen, rising star in *ECW*, The Miz. The unlikely tandem secured the WWE Tag Team Championship on *SmackDown* territory following the unique talent exchange arrangement between *SmackDown* and *ECW* managing officials. The 'Shaman of Sexy's' vanity reached new heights, much like his sports-entertainment career. After defeating his own tag team partner for a shot at the *Money In The Bank* contract, Morrison proved that he'll do whatever it takes to become the top Superstar in WWE today.

MONEY IN THE BANK
LADDER MATCH

"Here comes the former *ECW* Champion, CM Punk! He has got to be a favourite in this match!"

"Talking about guys who could win this, here is Mr Kennedy!"

"Next out to join John Morrison, Shelton Benjamin and Carlito is the cocky *SmackDown* Superstar, MVP."

"And the last man to enter the ring is Chris Jericho!"

"The match is underway, and MVP delivers a brutal-looking kick to John Morrison!"

"MVP is keeping everyone out of the ring with that ladder! Shelton Benjamin just caught a hard shot to the face."

"Everyone is on the outside, and look at this! John Morrison just hit a moonsault while holding a ladder. This is unbelievable!"

"John Morrison climbs the ladder, but it looks like Mr Kennedy has him hooked for a superplex!"

"What is Shelton doing? A sunset flip from the ladder and a superplex! I have never seen that before!"

"What an incredible move! The impact! The devastation!"

"Shelton Benjamin showing his athletic skills there! Perched on the top rope!"

"But CM Punk pulls him down and hits him with the GTS. The Go 2 Sleep!"

"Mr Kennedy just hit The Mic Check on top of the ladder. That move hurt both men!"

"Shelton Benjamin has made his way to the top of that giant ladder. But Mr Kennedy is trying to tip it over!"

"Shelton is going over the top rope and to the outside!"

"But look, there is another ladder out there! Shelton Benjamin just crashed through the ladder! He must be out of this match!"

"Jericho, Carlito and Kennedy are all atop of the ladder. Who will be able to reach up and grab that briefcase?"

"John Morrison breaks up the attempt and gets caught in The Walls Of Jericho on top of the ladder. This match is plain crazy!"

"Mr Kennedy is trying to take advantage of the situation, but all three men crash back down to the canvas!"

"MVP is about to grab the briefcase! But who is that! Matt Hardy! Hardy just hit MVP with the Twist Of Fate from the top of the ladder!"

27

"Carlito, Kennedy, Jericho and Punk are all on the ladders trying to secure the win, but Shelton Benjamin knocks all four men back down."

"What is John Morrison doing here? He could win this!"

"But Carlito knocks him off the ladder and to the outside!"

"Morrison crashes into a pile of used ladders and he must be out of this match! This is total carnage!"

"Carlito and Jericho are at the top of the ladder and Carlito sends Jericho crashing to the mat after a stiff right hand!"

"Carlito thought he had this match won, but Mr Kennedy just made it up the ladder to stop him and sends him flying back down on to yet another ladder!"

"Chris Jericho almost has the briefcase! Can he get hold of it? CM Punk is desperately trying to stop him!"

"Punk has climbed up the ladder and hung Jericho up in the Tree Of Woe! CM Punk has his hands on the case!"

"CM Punk has done it! He has the briefcase! CM Punk is *Mr Money In The Bank!*"

"CM Punk has done it! He can now cash in that contract anytime he wants!"

"I wonder if tonight will be the night that CM Punk faces a World Champion?"

"I think after that match, CM Punk would be wiser to wait until he has recovered!"

WRESTLEMANIA QUIZ

Q11. Which two Superstars faced of in a match billed as 'The Battle For Brand Supremacy'?

A. Undertaker & Shawn Michaels
B. Batista & Umaga
C. Shawn Michaels & Ric Flair

Q12. How tall is Batista?

A. 6-foot-2
B. 6-foot-4
C. 6-foot-5

Q13. From where does Umaga hail?

A. Samoa
B. Hawaii
C. Mexico

Q 14. Who did Batista face at *WrestleMania 23*?

A. John Cena
B. Undertaker
C. Edge

Q 15. Who was forced to have his head shaved as a result of Umaga losing his match at *WrestleMania 23*?

A. Mr McMahon
B. Shane McMahon
C. Linda McMahon

YOU'VE MADE IT TO ROUND TWO OF THE *WRESTLEMANIA* QUIZ...

Remember to keep on adding up your scores to see if you have what it takes to become a WWE Champion!

Q 16. Who did Chavo Guerrero defeat to win his first *ECW* Championship?

A. John Morrison
B. Big Show
C. CM Punk

Q 17. Who was Kane's tag team partner in the Brother's Of Destruction?

A. Big Show
B. Undertaker
C. Boogeyman

Q 18. At which *WrestleMania* did Chavo Guerrero team with his uncle, Eddie Guerrero, as part of the team, Los Guerreros?

A. *WrestleMania XX*
B. *WrestleMania X8*
C. *WrestleMania XIX*

Q 19. Who did Kane defeat for his only WWE Championship?

A. John Cena
B. The Rock
C. Stone Cold Steve Austin

Q 20. Including *WrestleMania XXIV*, how many *WrestleMania* appearances has Kane made?

A. 9
B. 11
C. 4

BATISTA

Height:
6-foot-5

Weight:
290 pounds

From:
Washington, DC

Signature Move:
Batista Bomb

There has always been a great rivalry between *Raw* and *SmackDown* and no one represents *SmackDown* better than the 'Animal,' Batista. Batista did not have an easy upbringing, living in a dangerous part of Washington DC. After a few brushes with the law, Batista found solace in the world of competitive body building. It was during a workout when a friend suggested he might give sports-entertainment a try. In 2002 he made his WWE debut and soon aligned himself with Triple H, Ric Flair and Randy Orton, forming the group, 'Evolution'. Since then he has been a World Heavyweight Champion, both a World Tag Team Champion and WWE Tag Team Champion, as well as a *Royal Rumble* winner. Batista is well qualified to defend *SmackDown's* honour, and only time will tell if he can defeat the 'Samoan Bulldozer.'

UMAGA

UMAGA

Height:
6-foot-4

Weight:
348 pounds

From:
The Isle of Samoa

Signature Move:
Samoan Spike

Originally brought to WWE in 2006 by Armando Estrada, Umaga comes from a long line of Samoans with a rich history – and a brutal path of destruction – in sports-entertainment. Immediately upon his debut, it was clear that the 'Samoan Bulldozer' would make a lasting impact, targeting and brutalizing WWE Hall of Famer 'Nature Boy' Ric Flair. Umaga was bloodthirsty and powerful. Flair and the rest of WWE knew at that moment a new monster was on the loose. Umaga is by far the rawest of all the *Raw* Superstars and will surely be more than up to the challenge of taking on the 'Animal!'

BATISTA vs UMAGA

"And here is his opponent, 'The Samoan Bulldozer' Umaga!"

"Here comes 'The Animal' Batista. Just listen to the reaction from the crowd."

"Both men look prepared for this match. This is going to be a war!"

"There you can see Theodore Long from *SmackDown*, the brand Batista is representing here tonight!"

"And don't forget about William Regal. I would not be surprised if he got involved in this match!"

"Umaga lands a stiff shot to the 'Animal's' head!"

"And Umaga sends Batista into the corner with some authority!"

"But Batista fires back with a huge boot to the face!"

"That really had to hurt the super heavyweight, Umaga!"

"But look at this! Umaga is straight back to his feet and tosses Batista over the top rope!"

"Batista is brought back into the ring by Umaga! And check this out! Umaga delivers a huge Samoan drop to the former champion!"

"Umaga has that nerve hold locked in! This will make your arm go to sleep in a matter of seconds."

"Batista is down on the mat! Umaga has made his way to the top rope. He is going for the big splash! But Batista moves out of the way!"

"Umaga is back to his feet, though! And he hits another Samoan drop!"

"Umaga is dragging Batista over to the corner. What can he be thinking?"

"Umaga charges at Batista, but Batista gets his foot up and delivers a huge boot to the face!"

"Again, though, Umaga seems to be unfazed and is going for the Samoan Spike! If he hits this move, the match will be over!"

"But Batista has caught Umaga's arm and is somehow holding him off!"

"Batista sends Umaga into the corner, and the Samoan caught his head on the ring post! How is Umaga still standing?"

WRESTLEMANIA

"Batista sends Umaga into the ropes and catches him with a huge spinebuster!"

"Batista is getting fired up here! This could be the end for Umaga!"

"Batista is going for the Batista Bomb! Surely, Umaga is just too big!"

"Batista is off balance! But look at that! Batista pulled off the Batista Bomb on the 300-plus pounder!"

"Just look at the impact! How did Batista do it? He is just so strong!"

"Batista is going for the cover! 1...2...3! Batista has done it! *SmackDown* has won this interpromotional match!"

"Theodore Long sure looks happy!"

"William Regal, on the other hand, looks like he is ready to get out of Orlando and go home!"

"So Batista gets the win at *WrestleMania XXIV!* What a match. Two great Superstars going head-to-head to prove which is the dominant brand!"

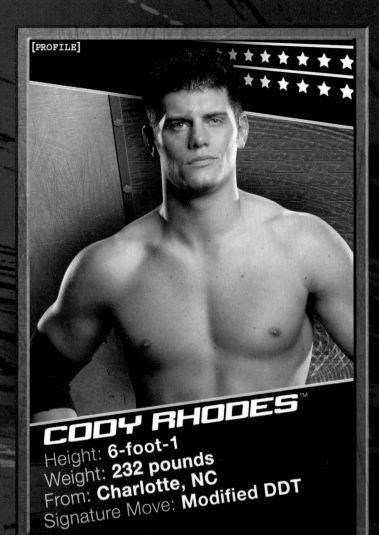

CODY RHODES™

Height: **6-foot-1**
Weight: **232 pounds**
From: **Charlotte, NC**
Signature Move: **Modified DDT**

LANCE CADE™

Height: **6-foot-5**
Weight: **261 pounds**
From: **Nashville, TN**
Signature Move: **Lariat Clothesline**

PAUL BURCHILL®

Height: **6-foot-4**
Weight: **247 pounds**
From: **Chelsea, England**
Signature Move: **Reverse swinging neckbreaker**

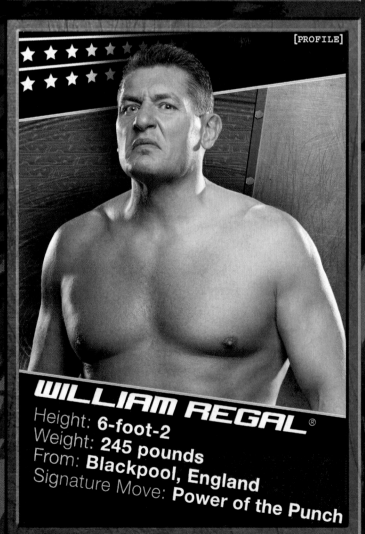

WILLIAM REGAL®

Height: **6-foot-2**
Weight: **245 pounds**
From: **Blackpool, England**
Signature Move: **Power of the Punch**

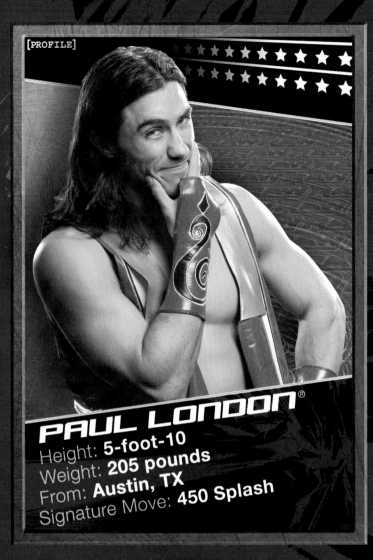

PAUL LONDON®

Height: **5-foot-10**
Weight: **205 pounds**
From: **Austin, TX**
Signature Move: **450 Splash**

CHARLIE HAAS®

Height: **6-foot-2**
Weight: **242 pounds**
From: **Edmond, OK**
Move: **Folding neck submission**

SNITSKY™

Height: **6-foot-8**
Weight: **307 pounds**
From: **Nesquehoning, PA**
Signature Move: **Pump-handle slam**

HARDCORE HOLLY™

Height: **6-foot**
Weight: **235 pounds**
From: **Mobile, AL**
Signature Move: **Alabama Slam**

WRESTLEMANIA QUIZ

Q21. At which event did Ric Flair make his *WrestleMania* debut?

A. *WrestleMania VIII*
B. *WrestleMania VII*
C. *WrestleMania XX*

Q22. Who did Ric Flair face at *WrestleMania X8*?

A. Undertaker
B. Mr McMahon
C. Triple H

Q23. Who did Shawn Michaels defeat for the WWE Championship at *WrestleMania XII*?

A. Stone Cold Steve Austin
B. Bret 'Hit Man' Hart
C. Undertaker

Q24. At which 2003 WWE PPV did Ric Flair and Shawn Michaels face each other for the very first time in singles competition?

A. *Unforgiven*
B. *No Way Out*
C. *Bad Blood*

Q25. Who announced Ric Flair as being the first inductee to the 2008 WWE Hall Of Fame?

A. Triple H
B. John Cena
C. Shawn Michaels

PART THREE OF THE *WRESTLEMANIA* QUIZ LOOKS AT THE MATCH THAT TOOK PLACE BETWEEN RIC FLAIR AND SHAWN MICHAELS.

As we know, if Flair were to lose the match, he would be forced to retire, ending the career of perhaps the greatest Superstar in the history of the industry.

Q26. In what year did Ric Flair make his professional debut?

A. 1980
B. 1972
C. 1979

Q27. Including *WrestleMania XXIV*, how many times has Shawn Michaels appeared at the event?

A. 16 times
B. 10 times
C. 19 times

Q28. Who did Shawn Michaels team with during his *WrestleMania* debut?

A. Triple H
B. Marty Jannetty
C. Warlord

Q29. What kind of match did Ric Flair compete in at *WrestleMania 22*?

A. *Steel Cage*
B. *Money in The Bank*
C. *Street Fight*

Q30. Who was the special guest referee for Shawn Michaels' match at *WrestleMania XIV*?

A. Ric Flair
B. Mike Tyson
C. Bart Gunn

KANE®

Height:
7 foot

Weight:
326 pounds

Signature Move:
Chokeslam

Kane earned the right to face Chavo Guerrero for the *ECW* Championship in a Battle Royal that took place before *WrestleMania XXIV*. During the match he defeated 23 other Superstars from *ECW*, *Raw* and *SmackDown*. Kane had only ever held a World Championship once before in his career, defeating Stone Cold Steve Austin for the WWE Championship at the 1998 *King Of The Ring*. He only managed to hold onto the title for one night before losing it back to the 'Texas Rattlesnake.' He has also held the WWE and World Tag Team Championship on several occasions and has also held the Hardcore Championship once and Intercontinental Championship twice. Going into his match with Chavo Guerrero, Kane has the obvious size and weight advantage, but with the match being held under *ECW* rules, some speculated that Chavo may have had the upper hand. Would Kane be extreme enough to be able to capture the *ECW* Championship, or would Chavo be able to cheat his way to another victory?

CHAVO GUERRERO™

Height:
5-foot-9

Weight:
210 pounds

From:
El Paso, TX

Signature Move:
Frog Splash, Gory Bomb

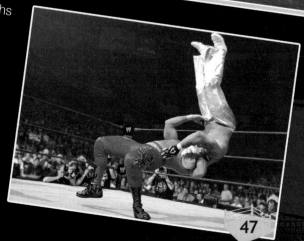

Chavo Guerrero captured the *ECW* Championship from CM Punk just two months before *WrestleMania XXIV*. It was not the first title Guerrero had held. He is a former multiple-time Cruiserweight Champion and WWE Tag Team Champion, not surprising when you consider his family's heritage. His gene line reads something out of wrestling history; his grandfather was the legendary wrestler and promoter Gory Guerrero and his late uncle, WWE Hall of Famer Eddie Guerrero, is a name that will resonate forever.

Winning the *ECW* Championship proved once and for all that no matter who he is with or against, Chavo is realizing his destiny as a member of one of the most celebrated families in sports-entertainment history.

"Well here comes the *ECW* Champion, Chavo Guerrero!"

"Earlier tonight, Kane won a Battle Royal for the right to face the champion for the title."

"Chavo looks pretty confident, though! You can bet Kane is going to be up for this match here tonight!"

"Chavo certainly is not endearing himself to the crowd!"

"And here comes Kane! Wait a second, where is he?"

"Chavo sure is not a popular champion! After defeating CM Punk for the *ECW* Championship, Chavo has not been a fan favourite!"

"Hold on! There he is! He came though the crowd!"

"Now Chavo has seen the 'Big Red Monster'!"

"I don't think that Chavo has any idea that Kane is right behind him!"

RIC

FLAIR
CHAMPIONSHIP HISTORY

RIC FLAIR HAS LONG BEEN THE BENCHMARK IN SPORTS-ENTERTAINMENT. MANY CONSIDER HIM TO BE THE GREATEST COMPETITOR OF ALL TIME, AND LOOKING AT HIS ACCOMPLISHMENTS, IT IS DIFFICULT TO ARGUE AGAINST THEM. CAPTURING HIS FIRST CHAMPIONSHIP IN 1974 AND HIS FINAL CHAMPIONSHIP IN 2006, RIC FLAIR HAS A TROPHY CABINET LIKE NO OTHER!

Mid-Atlantic Tag Team Championship, w/Rip Hawk, defeating Paul Jones & Bob Bruggers *(4TH July, 1974)*

Mid-Atlantic Television Championship, defeating Paul Jones *(1975)*

NWA World Tag Team Championship, w/Greg Valentine, defeating Gene & Ole Anderson *(26TH December 1976)*

Mid-Atlantic Television Championship, defeating Rufus R. Jones *(1977)*

Mid-Atlantic Tag Team Championship, w/Greg Valentine, defeating Dino Bravo & Tiger Conway Jr *(30TH June 1977)*

NWA United States Championship, defeating Bobo Brazil *(September 1977)*

NWA Tag Team Championship, w/Greg Valentine defeating Gene & Ole Anderson *(30TH October 1977)*

NWA United States Championship, defeating Mr Wrestling *(May 1978)*

NWA (Mid-Atlantic) Tag Team Championship, w/Big John Studd *(30TH June 1978)*

NWA Tag Team Championship, w/Big John Studd, defeating Paul Jones & Ricky Steamboat *(30TH October 1978)*

NWA United States Championship, defeating Ricky Steamboat *(1ST April 1979)*

NWA Tag Team Championship, w/Blackjack Mulligan, defeating Baron Von Raschke & Paul Jones *(8TH August 1979)*

NWA United States Championship, defeating Greg Valentine *(24TH November 1980)*

NWA United States Championship, defeating Jimmy Snuka *(19TH April 1981)*

NWA Championship, defeating Dusty Rhodes *(17TH September 1981)*

Missouri Heavyweight Championship, defeating David von Erich *(15TH July 1983)*

NWA Championship, defeating Harley Race *(24TH Novemeber 1983)*

NWA Championship, defeating Harley Race *(24TH March 1984)*

NWA Championship, defeating Kerry von Erich *(24TH May 1984)*

NWA Championship, defeating Dusty Rhodes *(7TH August 1986)*

NWA Championship, defeating Ron Garvin *(26TH November 1987)*

NWA Championship, defeating Ricky Steamboat *(7TH May 1989)*

NWA Championship, defeating Sting *(11TH January 1991)*

NWA Championship, defeating Tatsumi Fujinami *(19TH May 1991)*

WWE Championship, by winning the *Royal Rumble* *(19TH January 1992)*

WWE Championship, defeating Randy Savage *(1ST September 1992)*

NWA Championship, defeating Barry Windham *(18TH July 1993)*

WCW Championship, defeating Vader *(27TH December 1993)*

WCW Championship, defeating Ricky Steamboat *(24TH March 1994)*

WCW Championship, defeating Sting *(23RD June 1994)*

WCW Championship, defeating Randy Savage *(25TH December 1995)*

WCW Championship, defeating Randy Savage *(11TH February 1996)*

WCW United States Championship, defeating Konnan *(7TH July 1996)*

WCW Championship, defeating Hulk Hogan *(14TH March 1999)*

WCW Championship, defeating Jeff Jarrett *(15TH May 2000)*

WCW Championship, defeating Kevin Nash *(29TH May 2000)*

World Tag Team Championship, w/ Batista, defeating Dudley Boyz in a Tag Team Turmoil match *(Armageddon 2003)*

World Tag Team Championship, w/ Batista, defeating Booker T & Rob Van Dam *(22ND March 2004)*

WWE Intercontinental Championship, defeating Carlito *(18TH September 2005)*

World Tag Team Championship, w/Roddy Piper, defeating Spirit Squad *(5TH November 2006)*

RIC FLAIR®

Height:
6-foot-1

Weight:
243 pounds

From:
Charlotte, NC

Signature Move:
Figure-Four Leglock

Ric Flair is arguably the greatest Superstar ever to set foot in a ring. Flair has seen and done it all in his 35 year career, winning endless titles and defeating a list of Superstars that is too long to mention. However, Flair's greatest challenge would come at *WrestleMania XXIV*. For four months, Ric Flair lived his life in defiance of overwhelming odds. In November 2007, Mr McMahon told the 16-time World Champion that if he lost again, he would be forced to retire. Against all odds, Flair earned victories over reigning WWE Champion Randy Orton, Umaga, Triple H, William Regal, United States Champion MVP, Mr Kennedy and Mr McMahon. Yet, Flair felt he had to know whether he could still compete with the best, and challenged Shawn Michaels, a man he loves and respects, at *WrestleMania XXIV*. Would the 'Showstopper' prove too much to overcome, or could 'Slick Ric' live to see another day?

SHAWN MICHAELS®

H.B.K
Shawn Michaels ™

Height:
6-foot-1

Weight:
225 pounds

From:
San Antonio, TX

Signature Move:
Sweet Chin Music

Shawn Michaels may be the top Superstar of his generation, but there has always been one man that he has admired — Ric Flair. When HBK looks at Flair, he sees everything that he has ever wanted to be. When Flair challenged HBK to a Career Threatening Match at WrestleMania XXIV, HBK was at first reluctant. He did not want to be the man who ended his hero's career. Flair knows that HBK is one of the greatest Superstars to ever compete at WrestleMania. Perhaps no one has had more show-stealing, unforgettable matches on the 'Grandest Stage of Them All', and Flair saw HBK as his ultimate challenge. Meanwhile, Michaels knows that there has been perhaps no greater champion in history than Flair. HBK and 'Naitch' consider it an honour to wrestle each other, and on what better stage than WrestleMania XXIV?

Ric Flair VS H.B.K
Shawn Michaels

"Well, this is a historic moment! Shawn Michaels will face Ric Flair. The stipulations of the match state that if Flair loses, he will have to retire."

"The 'Heartbreak Kid' will be treating this match like the biggest of his career. There may not be a title up for grabs, but this is more important than any championship!"

"And here he is! 'Nature Boy' Ric Flair!"

"No one in the history of sports-entertainment has achieved as much as this man!"

"Ric Flair is one of the most loved Superstars in history! I can't imagine what WWE would be like without this man!"

"HBK and Flair are feeling each other out. Both men are being pretty cagey so far!"

"Flair sends HBK into the corner! But Michaels nips up onto the top rope!"

"HBK may be taking a page out of Flair's playbook here! Flair sends him crashing back down to the mat!"

"HBK is back to his feet, but Flair hits him with a chop block to the back of the knee!"

"HBK has recovered, though, and picks up Flair for a big bodyslam! And Flair rolls to the outside!"

"What is HBK thinking? He is on the top rope! He is going for a moonsault!"

"Just look at the elevation! HBK hits Flair with a perfect moonsault!"

"HBK escapes and has Flair down on the mat! HBK is climbing to the top!"

"HBK just hit an elbow from the top rope! Could this be it?"

"Look at Flair urging HBK to bring it on!"

"HBK may be tuning up the band here! This could be the end for Flair!"

"If Flair is going out, he's going to go out just as he's carried himself his entire career — a true champion".

"HBK is making the pin! 1...2...3! It's over! The long and storied career of Ric Flair is over!"

"This has to be a bittersweet win for Shawn Michaels, and he can't hide it. No one wanted to see Ric Flair lose here tonight!"

"This is the end for the 'Nature Boy' after decades of being 'The Man.' You have just witnessed Flair's final match!"

"Goodbye, 'Nature Boy'. And thank you."

"Flair is back to his feet! The emotion that must be pumping through his veins right now!"

BETH PHOENIX™ & MELINA™

Name:
Beth Phoenix

From:
Buffalo, NY

Career Highlight:
WWE Women's Champion

Name:
Melina

From:
Los Angeles, CA

Career Highlight:
WWE Women's Champion

Melina

Beth Phoenix

Leading up to *WrestleMania XXIV*, Melina and Beth Phoenix challenged Maria and Ashley to a *Playboy BunnyMania Lumberjack Match*. The pair were angered by all the attention Maria had received since she posed in *Playboy* just a month before the event. The 'Glamazon' & Melina want to batter Maria & Ashley's pretty faces. These two Divas believe Ashley and Maria had their fame and prestige handed to them. Melina and Beth came up, as they would tell you, 'the hard way' and spent years honing their craft. Beth Phoenix especially wants to prove a point at *WrestleMania XXIV*. She believes she is the 'uber-Diva', the epitome of beauty, grace and skill. To Beth, Ashley and Maria are pretenders to her throne, and she wants to vanquish both of them at the 'uber-event' in sports-entertainment.

WWeU

MARIA & ASHLEY™®

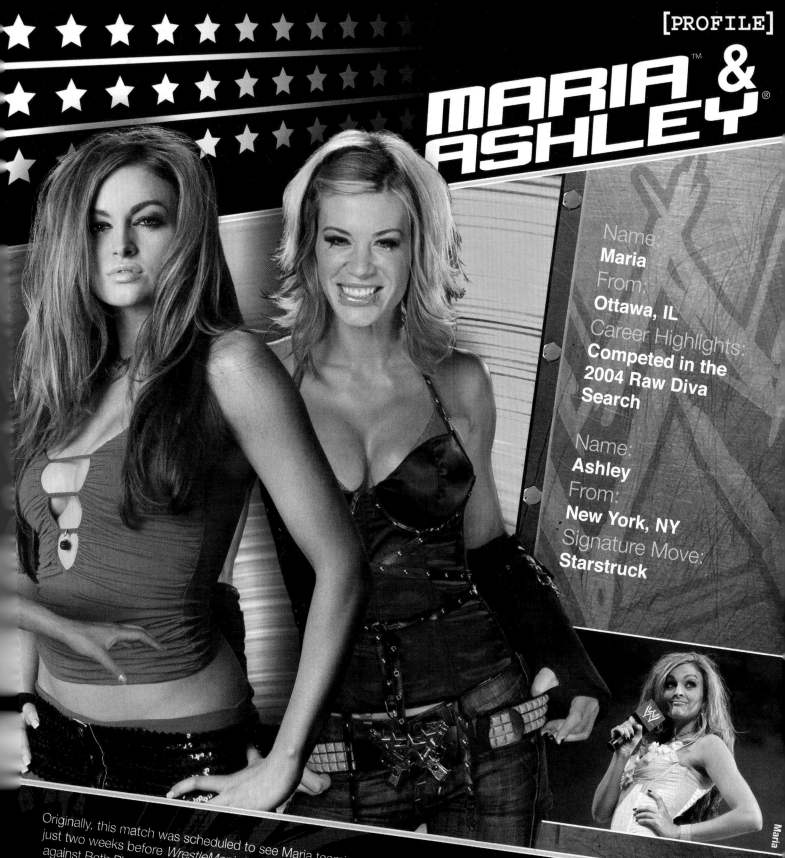

Name:
Maria
From:
Ottawa, IL
Career Highlights:
Competed in the
2004 Raw Diva
Search

Name:
Ashley
From:
New York, NY
Signature Move:
Starstruck

Maria

Ashley

Originally, this match was scheduled to see Maria teaming with Candice. However, just two weeks before *WrestleMania XXIV*, Candice broke her clavicle in a match against Beth Phoenix. While Maria desperately searched for a replacement partner, another former *Playboy* cover girl had been waiting in the wings.

Ashley stands for everything the 'Glamazon' and her tag team partner can't stand. Her looks landed her on the cover of *Playboy* last year. Still, she packs with her the skills to hold her own in the ring, and *WrestleMania XXIV* is her opportunity to show them off.

Maria also wants to prove that she is much more than a pretty face. Maria has worked hard at becoming a force in WWE inside and outside the ring. *Playboy's* new cover girl is ready and willing to show Beth Phoenix and Melina that she has many tricks up her sleeve.

65

WWE**Divas**

DIVAS BUNNYMANIA LUMBERJILL MATCH

WRESTLEMANIA XXIV

"The 'Doggfather' is in the house!"

"Here comes our master of ceremonies for tonight's Diva *Playboy BunnyMania Lumberjill* match, rap icon Snoop Dogg!"

"Just look at the lovely Divas he is bringing to the ring with him! All three brands, *ECW*, *Raw* and *SmackDown* are represented here tonight!"

"There is Jillian and Katie Lea making their way to ringside! This is going to be awesome!"

"And Snoop Dogg looks to be in his element!"

"Here come the first two participants for tonight's match, Maria and Ashley!"

"Originally, Maria was to be teaming with, Candice Michelle, but Candice is out injured with a broken collarbone!"

"And here are their opponents! Melina and Beth Phoenix! What is Santino Marella doing with them?"

"Never mind Santino! How good does Melina look?"

"At this present moment, I think he thinks he is the man!"

"I just can't stand Santino Marella! Just who does he think he is?"

"The match is underway, and Ashley just ducked a clothesline attempt from Beth Phoenix!"

"Phoenix does not look happy here! Ashley is using her quickness to avoid the 'Glamazon'!"

"Ashley makes the tag to Maria and she delivers a big boot to Beth Phoenix's gut!"

"Bronco Buster from Maria! Melina is in trouble in the corner!"

"Ashley and Melina are now in the ring and Ashley catches Melina with a head scissors takedown!"

"But Ashley has been sent to the outside and the other Divas are brutally attacking her! They are not meant to do that! They should just send her back into the ring!"

"Ashley is back in the ring and Beth Phoenix catches her in a huge bearhug!"

"Look at this teamwork from Melina and Beth Phoenix! A moonsault from the shoulders of her partner!"

"Ashley makes the tag to Maria, and Maria takes Beth Phoenix down with a hurricanrana!"

"Maria might be going for a bulldog here!"

"Look at this! Ashley just leapt from the ring apron and has taken out half of the Lumberjills on the outside!"

"Maria with a cross-body block from the top! She is going for the pin! But look at this! Santino Marella just broke up the pin!"

"Beth Phoenix just hit Maria with a pump-handle slam! This match is over! 1...2...3!"

"Check this out! Snoop Dogg has taken exception to Santino Marella and just hit him with a brutal-looking clothesline!"

"Well, Maria may have lost the match, but I think that Snoop has taken a real shine to her!"

WRESTLEMANIA QUIZ

Q31. In what year did Ashley win the *Raw* Diva Search Contest?

A. 2004
B. 2005
C. 2006

Q32. Who did Melina face at *WrestleMania 23*?

A. Ashley
B. Candice
C. Maria

Q33. With which former Intercontinental Champion was Maria once romantically involved?

A. Edge
B. Shelton Benjamin
C. Santino Marella

Q34. Who did Melina defeat for the Women's Championship in Paris, France in 2007?

A. Ashley
B. Candice
C. Mickie James

Q35. Who did Beth Phoenix defeat for her first WWE Women's Championship?

A. Mickie James
B. Candice
C. Melina

SO HOW ARE YOU DOING IN THE *WRESTLEMANIA* QUIZ? TOUGH, ISN'T IT?

Well, in part four, we continue to look at some of the great matches and Superstars from *WrestleMania XXIV*. See how you do!

Q36. Who did Randy Orton team with to defeat Ric Flair & 'Rowdy' Roddy Piper for the World Tag Team Championships?

A. Edge
B. Batista
C. Triple H

Q37. Who did Randy Orton defeat in his *SmackDown* debut in 2002?

A. John Cena
B. Hardcore Holly
C. Shane McMahon

Q38. In what year did John Cena introduce the 'Spinner' version of the WWE Championship?

A. 2004
B. 2005
C. 2006

Q39. Who defeated Triple H to retain his WWE Championship at *WrestleMania 22*?

A. John Cena
B. Randy Orton
C. Undertaker

Q40. What was Triple H known as when he debuted for WWE?

A. Horrid Henry-Helmsley
B. Hunter Hearst-Helmsley
C. Hillbilly Hal-Hemsley

CHUCK PALUMBO®

Height: **6-foot-7**
Weight: **280 pounds**
From: **San Diego, CA**
Signature Move: **Full Throttle**

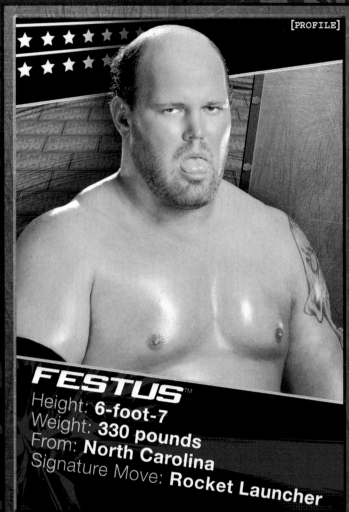

FESTUS™

Height: **6-foot-7**
Weight: **330 pounds**
From: **North Carolina**
Signature Move: **Rocket Launcher**

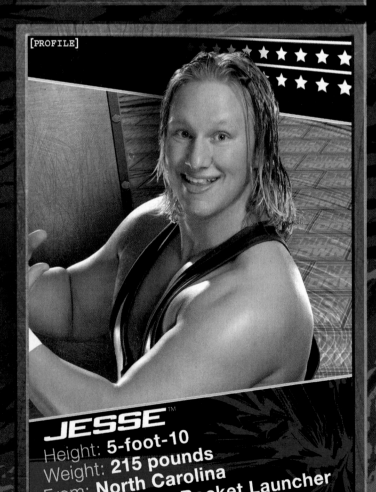

JESSE™

Height: **5-foot-10**
Weight: **215 pounds**
From: **North Carolina**
Signature Move: **Rocket Launcher**

JAMIE NOBLE™

Height: **5-foot-9**
Weight: **202 pounds**
From: **Hanover, WV**
Signature Move: **Modified Dragon Sleeper**

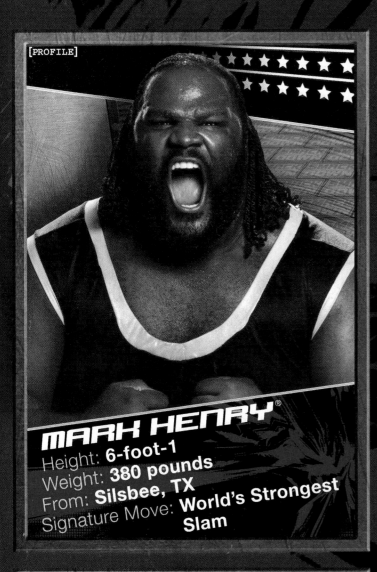

MARK HENRY®

Height: **6-foot-1**
Weight: **380 pounds**
From: **Silsbee, TX**
Signature Move: **World's Strongest Slam**

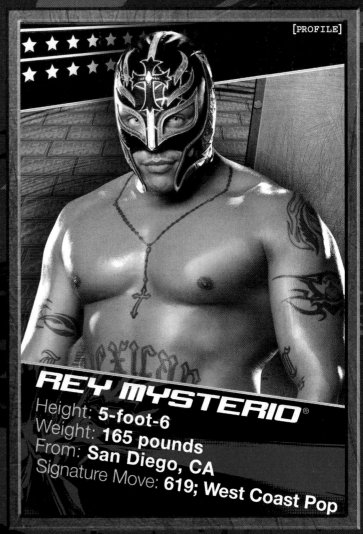

REY MYSTERIO®

Height: **5-foot-6**
Weight: **165 pounds**
From: **San Diego, CA**
Signature Move: **619; West Coast Pop**

MICK FOLEY™

Height: **6-foot-2**
Weight: **287 pounds**
From: **Long Island, NY**
Signature Move: **Mandible Claw**

THE GREAT KHALI®

Height: **7-foot-3**
Weight: **420 pounds**
From: **India**
Signature Move: **Khali Vise Grip**

RANDY ORTON®

Height:
6-foot-4

Weight:
245 pounds

From:
St. Louis

Signature Move:
RKO

His father is WWE Hall of Famer 'Cowboy' Bob Orton, and his grandfather was 'The Big O', the late Bob Orton, Sr. Most kids remember their first ball game or school play; Randy's childhood memories include sitting in the kitchen of his family's St Louis home with 'Rowdy' Roddy Piper and Greg 'The Hammer' Valentine, and repairing a broken banister leaned on by Andre the Giant. He wasn't even five years old when he watched his father inadvertently knock out 'Mr Wonderful' Paul Orndorff in the main event at the inaugural *WrestleMania*, but he already knew he wanted to be a WWE Superstar. And ever since his WWE debut in 2002, Orton has been trying to live up to his family's legacy. Becoming the youngest World Heavyweight Champion in history was just the start. Orton has destroyed legends with far more experience, and has proven to be one of the most dominant champions in recent history. Facing his old 'Evolution' stablemate, Triple H, and former WWE Champion John Cena, will not phase the cocky young Superstar when *WrestleMania XXIV* rolls around.

TRIPLE H

Height:
6-foot-4

Weight:
260 pounds

From:
Greenwich, CT

Signature Move:
Pedigree

For a moment, forget all the monikers, 'The Game', 'The Cerebral Assassin', and consider what Triple H has accomplished in his career. A former WWE Champion, World Heavyweight Champion, Intercontinental Champion, World Tag Team Champion, European Champion, King of the Ring winner (1997) and *Royal Rumble* winner (2002), Triple H has done it all. Since his debut in 1995, Triple H has solidified his place at the top of the ladder in WWE. At *WrestleMania XXIV*, Triple H would face two men that he knows all too well. At *WrestleMania 22*, John Cena defeated Triple H in a hard-fought match, while it was Triple H who ended Randy Orton's first title reign. Add to that the fact that Triple H took Orton under his wing as a part of 'Evolution' early in his career and it becomes hard to argue that Triple H doesn't have the advantage going into the Triple Threat Match at *WrestleMania XXIV*.

JOHN CENA®

JOHN·CENA™

Height:
6-foot-1

Weight:
240 pounds

From:
West Newbury, MA

Signature Moves:
FU; STFU

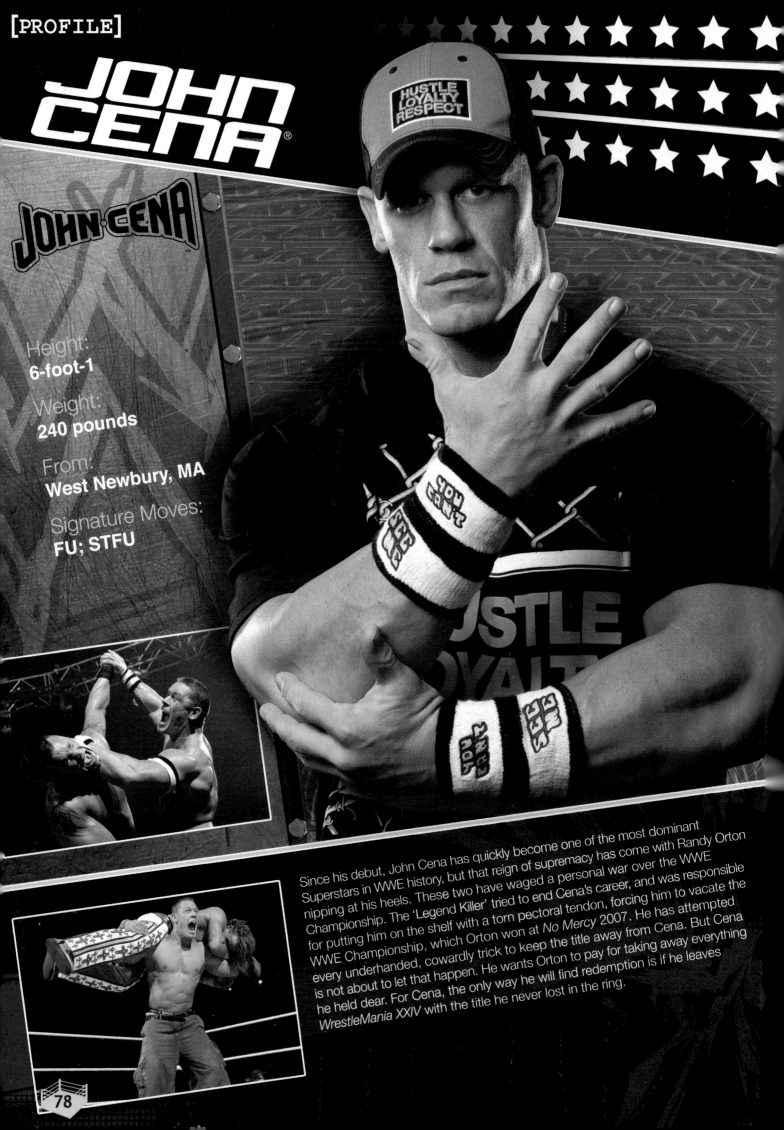

Since his debut, John Cena has quickly become one of the most dominant Superstars in WWE history, but that reign of supremacy has come with Randy Orton nipping at his heels. These two have waged a personal war over the WWE Championship. The 'Legend Killer' tried to end Cena's career, and was responsible for putting him on the shelf with a torn pectoral tendon, forcing him to vacate the WWE Championship, which Orton won at *No Mercy 2007*. He has attempted every underhanded, cowardly trick to keep the title away from Cena. But Cena is not about to let that happen. He wants Orton to pay for taking away everything he held dear. For Cena, the only way he will find redemption is if he leaves *WrestleMania XXIV* with the title he never lost in the ring.

"John Cena is making his way to the ring!"

"Cena walks out to quite a mixed reaction!"

"Triple H truly believes he deserves the title, and you can bet that he will be fired up for this match!"

"But listen to this! Triple H, 'The Game' is in the building, and I think it is quite obvious who the fans are rooting for in this match!"

"Triple H looks to be in the best shape of his life! And he won't be intimidated by any of his opponents here at *WrestleMania!*"

79

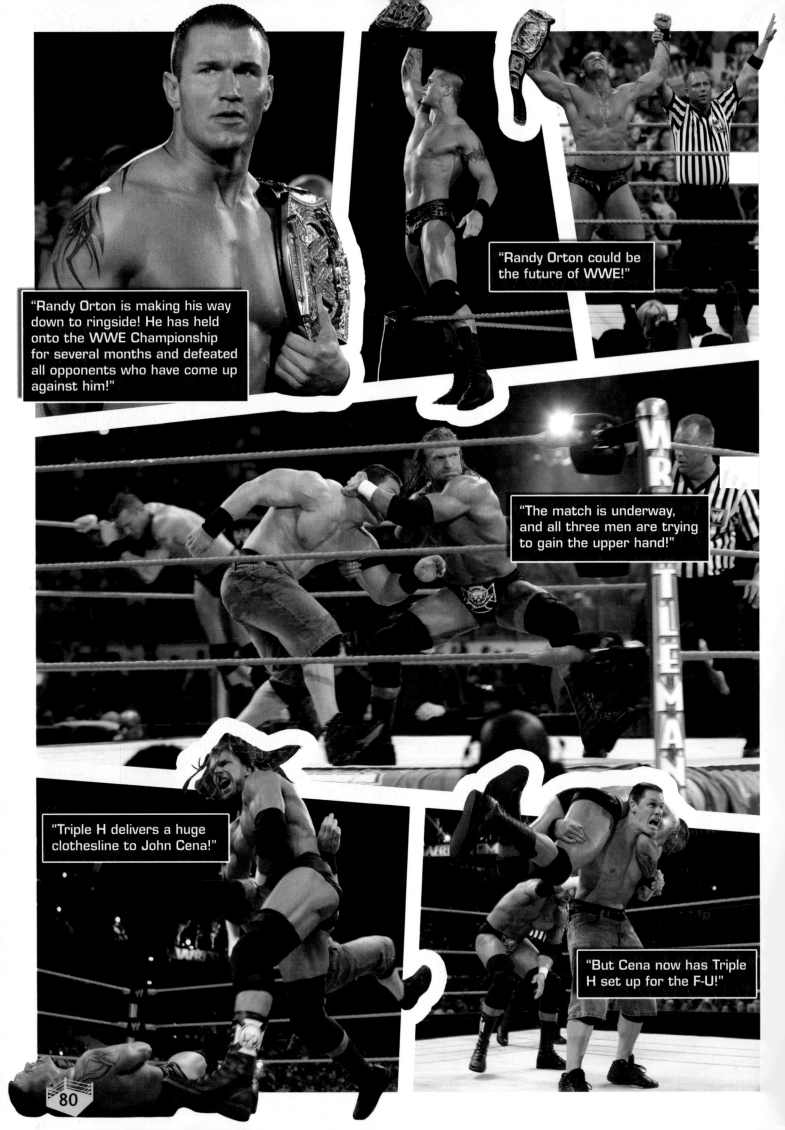

"Randy Orton is making his way down to ringside! He has held onto the WWE Championship for several months and defeated all opponents who have come up against him!"

"Randy Orton could be the future of WWE!"

"The match is underway, and all three men are trying to gain the upper hand!"

"Triple H delivers a huge clothesline to John Cena!"

"But Cena now has Triple H set up for the F-U!"

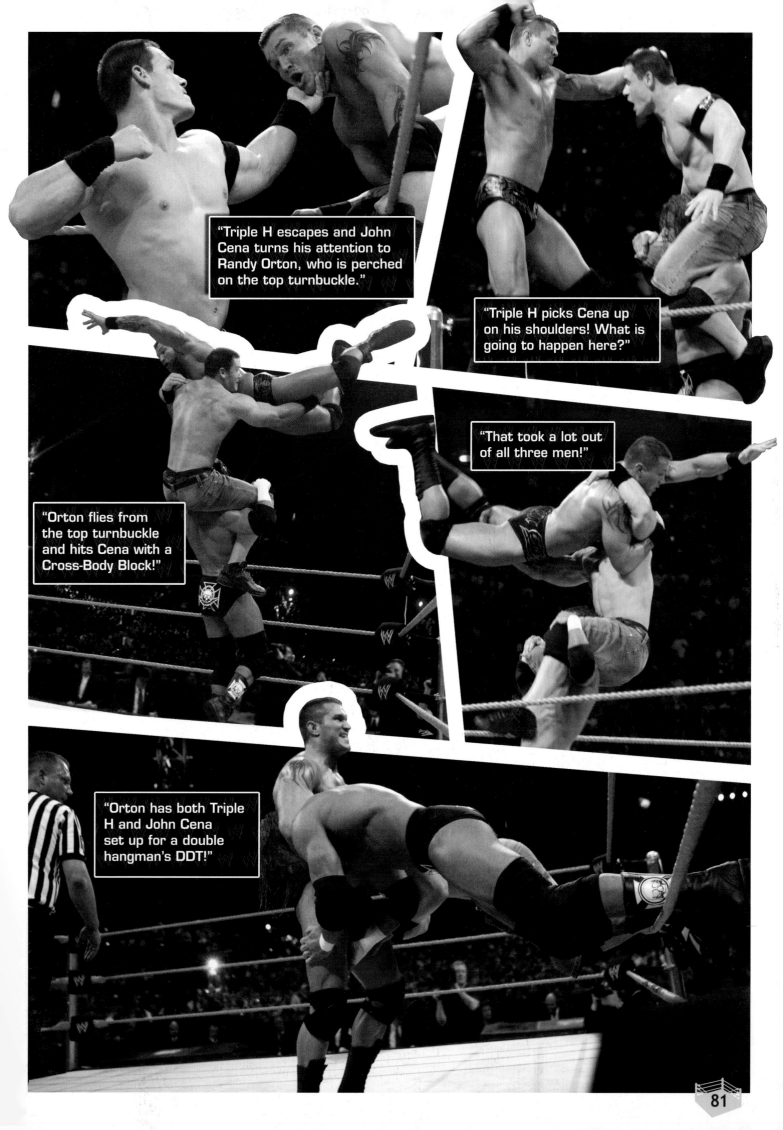

"Triple H escapes and John Cena turns his attention to Randy Orton, who is perched on the top turnbuckle."

"Triple H picks Cena up on his shoulders! What is going to happen here?"

"That took a lot out of all three men!"

"Orton flies from the top turnbuckle and hits Cena with a Cross-Body Block!"

"Orton has both Triple H and John Cena set up for a double hangman's DDT!"

"Triple H breaks it up just before Orton can tap out!"

"Look at Cena, though! He refuses to break the hold! Triple H has John Cena in the crossface! Can Cena survive here?"

"As Orton rolls out of the ring, Triple H hits Cena with the facebuster!"

"And he follows up with a huge clothesline that almost incapacitates Cena!"

"Triple H is going for the pin! 1...2...! Orton broke up the pin with a devastating kick to the face! Orton is going for the pin himself! 1...2...3! Orton retains the title!"

"Orton has just barely held onto his title!"

"And you can see from the look on his face that he is so happy that the match is over!"

WRESTLEMANIA CROSSWORD

HOW MUCH OF A WWE FAN ARE YOU? CAN YOU WORK OUT ALL OF THE CRYPTIC CLUES TO DECIPHER THE *WRESTLEMANIA* LEGENDS BELOW?

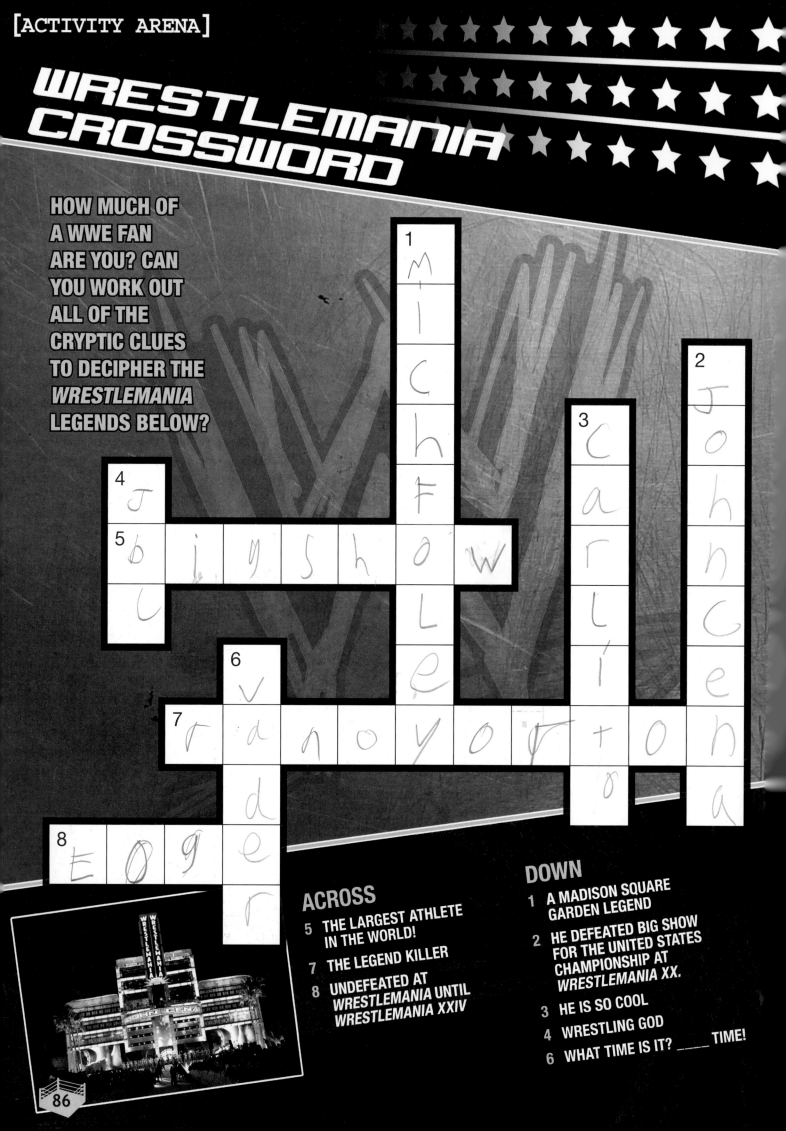

1 M I C H F O L E Y

2 J o h n C e n a

3 C a r l i t o

4 J
5 b i g s h o w
b
c

6 v
7 r a n d y o r t o n
a
d
e
8 E d g e r

ACROSS

5 THE LARGEST ATHLETE IN THE WORLD!

7 THE LEGEND KILLER

8 UNDEFEATED AT WRESTLEMANIA UNTIL WRESTLEMANIA XXIV

DOWN

1 A MADISON SQUARE GARDEN LEGEND

2 HE DEFEATED BIG SHOW FOR THE UNITED STATES CHAMPIONSHIP AT WRESTLEMANIA XX.

3 HE IS SO COOL

4 WRESTLING GOD

6 WHAT TIME IS IT? _____ TIME!

WRESTLEMANIA WORD SEARCH

HOW MANY *WRESTLEMANIA* LEGENDS CAN YOU FIND IN THE WORD SEARCH BELOW?

J	W	H	L	G	S	K	G	R	P	P	C	C	T	E	D	L	X
A	D	A	I	K	A	Y	C	E	D	H	V	T	C	U	U	N	E
K	I	O	N	L	C	J	J	A	E	S	A	A	S	N	C	T	G
E	N	A	A	S	L	Z	A	N	J	S	U	T	J	H	A	O	A
R	N	A	R	G	P	H	B	U	T	Z	S	Y	Q	O	M	D	A	R
O	A	B	G	C	X	L	I	S	O	R	U	L	C	L	H	E	O
B	O	R	U	T	S	K	A	L	H	O	V	T	L	M	D	P	Y
E	T	E	D	S	C	V	Z	O	L	P	D	U	C	A	C	G	Z
R	T	P	M	G	H	R	D	J	K	Y	B	B	V	A	X	F	M
T	D	I	I	C	U	E	R	F	B	H	J	N	C	G	C	E	X
S	W	P	J	H	S	D	T	D	S	E	S	I	S	R	Y	T	W
L	V	Y	W	Q	B	U	J	I	R	X	H	W	M	G	K	P	X
N	R	D	A	V	I	A	T	A	S	K	B	D	Q	D	U	R	F
X	Z	D	S	Y	B	I	L	N	C	N	W	B	B	A	G	R	M
N	Z	O	K	Z	R	A	K	U	N	S	Y	M	M	I	J	B	E
X	Q	R	C	B	S	G	T	S	L	A	U	G	H	T	E	R	Y
I	K	R	A	Q	Q	L	B	R	K	T	N	L	X	B	L	M	X
E	F	Z	H	B	A	Z	G	T	Q	F	M	T	T	S	Q	N	C

Answers on page 92

- BRITISH BULLDOG
- CACTUS JACK
- DUSTY RHODES
- HACKSAW JIM DUGGAN
- HILLBILLY JIM
- JAKE ROBERTS
- JIMMY SNUKA
- RODDY PIPER
- SGT SLAUGHTER
- VADER

87

WRESTLEMANIA
SPOT THE DIFFERENCE

Take a look at this classic match between John Cena and Shawn Michaels. Both images may look the same but our dastardly designers have made ten subtle changes! Can you spot them all?

Answers on page 93.

SIGNATURE MOVES

?	FU 4
?	619 3
?	Pedigree 5
?	Old School 1
?	Batista Bomb 2
?	Sweet Chin Music 6

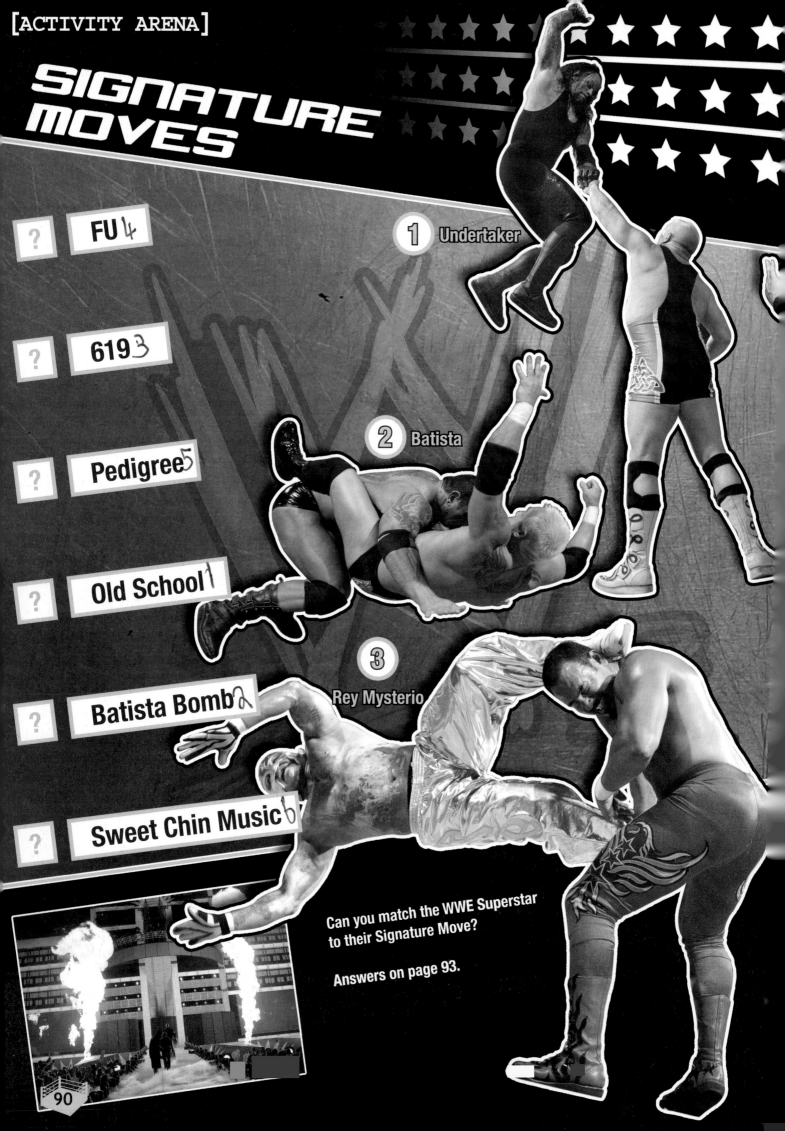

1 Undertaker

2 Batista

3 Rey Mysterio

Can you match the WWE Superstar to their Signature Move?

Answers on page 93.

5 Triple H

4 John Cena

6 Shawn Michaels

ANSWERS

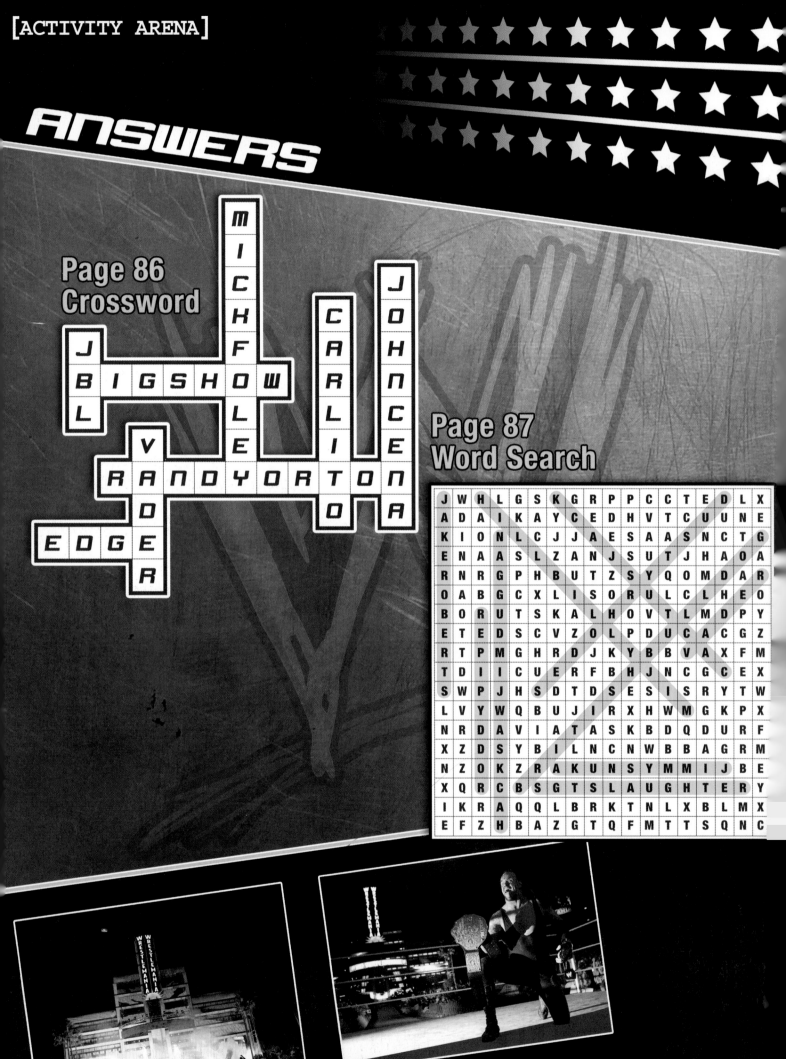

Page 86
Crossword

MICK FOLEY

JBL

BIGSHOW

CARLITO

JOHN CENA

RANDY ORTON

VADER

EDGE

Page 87
Word Search

J	W	H	L	G	S	K	G	R	P	P	C	C	T	E	D	L	X
A	D	A	I	K	A	Y	C	E	D	H	V	T	C	U	U	N	E
K	I	O	N	L	C	J	J	A	E	S	A	A	S	N	C	T	G
E	N	A	A	S	L	Z	A	N	J	S	U	T	J	H	A	O	A
R	N	R	G	P	H	B	U	T	Z	S	Y	Q	O	M	D	A	R
O	A	B	G	C	X	L	I	S	O	R	U	L	C	L	H	E	O
B	O	R	U	T	S	K	A	L	H	O	V	T	L	M	D	P	Y
E	T	E	D	S	C	V	Z	O	L	P	D	U	C	A	C	G	Z
R	T	P	M	G	H	R	D	J	K	Y	B	B	V	A	X	F	M
T	D	I	I	C	U	E	R	F	B	H	J	N	C	G	C	E	X
S	W	P	J	H	S	D	T	D	S	E	S	I	S	R	Y	T	W
L	V	Y	W	Q	B	U	J	I	R	X	H	W	M	G	K	P	X
N	R	D	A	V	I	A	T	A	S	K	B	D	Q	D	U	R	F
X	Z	D	S	Y	B	I	L	N	C	N	W	B	B	A	G	R	M
N	Z	O	K	Z	R	A	K	U	N	S	Y	M	M	I	J	B	E
X	Q	R	C	B	S	G	T	S	L	A	U	G	H	T	E	R	Y
I	K	R	A	Q	Q	L	B	R	K	T	N	L	X	B	L	M	X
E	F	Z	H	B	A	Z	G	T	Q	F	M	T	T	S	Q	N	C

Page 88-89 Spot The Difference

Page 90-91 Signature Moves
1. Old School, 2. Batista Bomb 3. 619, 4. FU,
5. Pedigree, 6. Sweet Chin Music.

MICKIE JAMES

Height: 6-foot-7
From: Richmond, VA
Signature Move: Mick Kick

CANDICE

From: Milwaukee, WI
Career Highlight: Women's Champion

CHERRY

From: The Other Side of the Tracks

LENA YADA

From: Honolulu, HI

MARYSE™

From: **Montreal, Quebec, Canada**

MICHELLE McCOOL®

From: **Palatka, FL**

LAYLA™

From: **Miami, Fla**

VICTORIA™

From: **San Bernardino, CA**
Signature Move: **Widow's Peak**
Career Highlight: **Women's Champion**

BIG DADDY V

Height: **6-foot-9**
Weight: **487 pounds**
From: **Harlem, NY**
Signature Move: **Big Daddy V Drop**

COLIN DELANEY

Height: **5-foot-10**
Weight: **172 pounds**
From: **Rochester, NY**

MATT STRIKER

Height: **5-foot-10**
Weight: **237 pounds**
From: **New York, NY**

KOFI KINGSTON

Height: **6-foot-1**
Weight: **225 pounds**
From: **Jamaica**

NUNZIO™

Height: **5-foot-7**
Weight: **170 pounds**
From: **Rockland County, NY**
Signature Move: **Sicilian Slice**

TOMMY DREAMER®

Height: **6-foot-2**
Weight: **255 pounds**
From: **Yonkers, NY**
Signature Move: **Dreamer Driver; DDT**

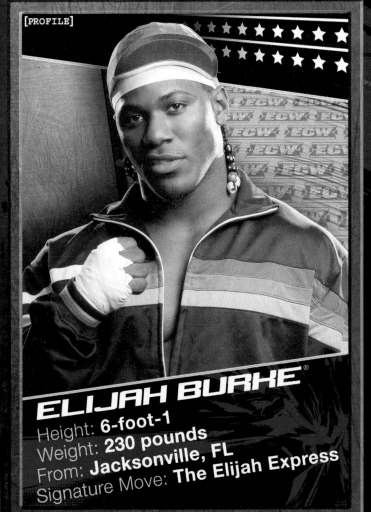

ELIJAH BURKE®

Height: **6-foot-1**
Weight: **230 pounds**
From: **Jacksonville, FL**
Signature Move: **The Elijah Express**

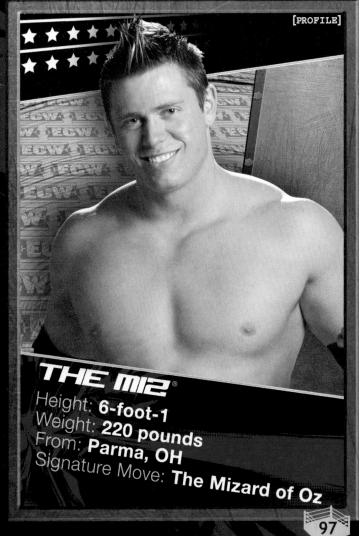

THE MIZ®

Height: **6-foot-1**
Weight: **220 pounds**
From: **Parma, OH**
Signature Move: **The Mizard of Oz**

WRESTLEMANIA QUIZ

Q41. During which WWE event did Big Show make his return in 2008?

A. *No Mercy*
B. *No Way Out*
C. *Survivor Series*

Q42. In which weight division does Floyd 'Money' Mayweather fight?

A. Heavyweight
B. Welterweight
C. Middleweight

Q43. In what year did Big Show debut in WWE?

A. 1990
B. 1999
C. 2000

Q44. Who did Big Show face at *WrestleMania XX*?

A. John Cena
B. Triple H
C. Undertaker

Q45. Who did Big Show defeat to win his first ECW Championship?

A. Rob Van Dam
B. CM Punk
C. Tazz

ITS THE FINAL PART OF THE WRESTLEMANIA QUIZ!

We are going to take a look at the match that took place between Big Show and Floyd 'Money' Mayweather and the main event of *WrestleMania XXIV*, Edge against Undertaker.

Q46. Who did Undertaker face at *WrestleMania VII*?

A. Hacksaw Jim Duggan
B. Hillbilly Jim
C. Jimmy "Superfly" Snuka

Q47. What kind of match did Undertaker compete in at *WrestleMania 22*?

A. *Steel Cage Match*
B. *Casket Match*
C. *TLC Match*

Q48. Who did Edge defeat to win his first WWE Championship?

A. JBL
B. Triple H
C. John Cena

Q49. In what year did Edge win *The King Of The Ring* Tournament?

A. 2000
B. 2001
C. 2003

Q50. How many times have Edge and Undertaker faced each other at previous *WrestleManias*?

A. Once
B. Twice
C. Never

Answers 41-B, 42-B, 43-B, 44-A, 45-A, 46-C, 47-B, 48-C, 49-B, 50-C

EDGE®

EDG3

Height:
6-foot-5

Weight:
240 pounds

From:
Toronto, Ontario, Canada

Signature Move:
Spear

When Edge made his WWE debut in June 1998, there were doubters who believed he wouldn't last. So he made his opponents believe, even if it meant taking chairs to the head, falling off ladders and crashing through tables. He's suffered a torn ACL, ruptured labra, a broken neck, a fractured skull, metal rods in his teeth and countless stitches over the years, but not without giving as good as he's received. More than the WWE Championship reigns or his time as World Heavyweight Champion, it is the sheer tenacity that Edge displays that will endure long after his days in the ring are over. Ask any man or woman who has gone toe-to-toe with him; they'll tell you why he's called the 'Rated-R Superstar'.

When Edge cashed in his *Money in The Bank* contract, taking advantage of an already battered and bloodied Undertaker, he captured his first World Heavyweight Championship. Undertaker has never forgotten that night, and almost a year later, at *WrestleMania XXIV*, the 'Deadman' will have his chance for revenge.

UNDERTAKER®

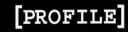

Undertaker

Height:
6-foot-10 1/2
Weight:
295 pounds
From:
Death Valley
Signature Move:
**Chokeslam;
Tombstone;
Last Ride**

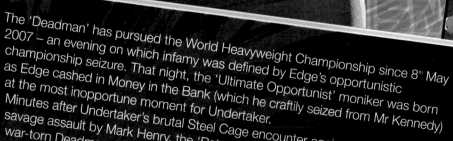

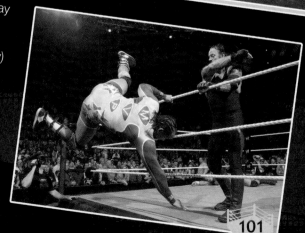

The 'Deadman' has pursued the World Heavyweight Championship since 8th May 2007 – an evening on which infamy was defined by Edge's opportunistic championship seizure. That night, the 'Ultimate Opportunist' moniker was born as Edge cashed in Money in the Bank (which he craftily seized from Mr Kennedy) at the most inopportune moment for Undertaker. Minutes after Undertaker's brutal Steel Cage encounter against Batista and a savage assault by Mark Henry, the 'Rated-R Superstar' stole the title from the war-torn Deadman. Edge continued to be a bane to Undertaker for months on SmackDown, keeping the 'Deadman' from reclaiming the championship. Now, nearly one year later, life proves to be ironically cyclical for Edge, as his date with the devil has been inked for WrestleMania XXIV. Undertaker's unmatched 15-0 record at WrestleMania casts an ominous, intimidating shadow over the 'Ultimate Opportunist's' reign. But, this imminent collision isn't about streaks, it's about the World Heavyweight Championship.

"The 'Deadman' is in the building! Undertaker has such a great record at WrestleMania. Will he be able to keep it here tonight against Edge?"

"No matter how many times I see Undertaker enter the ring, it always gives me chills."

"And here comes the World Heavyweight Champion, Edge!"

"With Vickie Guerrero on his side, you have to give the advantage to the champion!"

"The 'Rated-R Superstar' is making one hell of an entrance here tonight!"

"Edge holds the World Heavyweight Championship up high above his head. That belt means everything to him!"

"Undertaker is signaling to Edge that his title reign may soon be over!"

"Edge with a huge shoulder to the gut of Undertaker in the corner!"

"Edge is going to work on the lower back and knee of Undertaker!"

"He is really synching in on the single-leg Boston Crab! Undertaker will not tap out, though!"

"Edge with a devastating dropkick right to the jaw of the challenger!"

"And he follows up with a reverse neckbreaker which snaps Undertaker's head into the canvas!"

"Edge comes straight back on the offensive with a spear out of nowhere!"

"Undertaker is back to his feet though, and goes Old School from the top rope, which sends the champ reeling."

"Edge goes to the outside to catch his breath. Undertaker with a suicide dive over the top rope!"

"Undertaker has Edge set for the guillotine leg drop on the ring apron! What a devastating manoeuvre!"

"Both men are back in the ring and Edge has gone back to the Boston Crab!"

"Edge hits Undertaker with a spinning heel kick! Edge is just so athletic!"

"What is Edge planning here? Undertaker just rose from the dead and has grabbed the champion by the throat!"

"Chokeslam! Chokeslam!"

"Undertaker has Edge held high in the air! And he sends him crashing to the canvas!"

"Undertaker is signaling that this is the end for Edge!"

"Undertaker has Edge locked into that chokehold of his! Will Edge tap out?"

"Edge made it to the ropes, but Undertaker has him set up for the Last Ride!"

"Undertaker has Edge in the triangle choke submission hold! Edge submits, Undertaker wins! Undertaker wins!"

"Undertaker has won the World Heavyweight Championship!"

"Undertaker has also kept his undefeated record at *WrestleMania!* He's a perfect 16-0!"

"The 'Deadman' has just defeated Edge for the World Heavyweight Championship! The 'Phenom' reigns supreme at *WrestleMania* once again!"

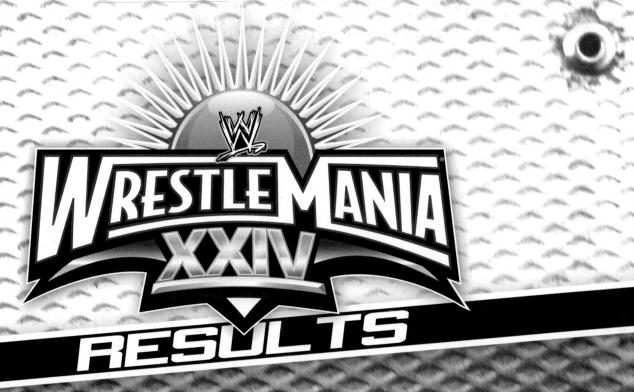

RESULTS

TRIPLE THREAT MATCH FOR THE WWE CHAMPIONSHIP
Randy Orton defeated John Cena and Triple H

WORLD HEAVYWEIGHT CHAMPIONSHIP MATCH
Undertaker defeated Edge

THE BIGGEST VS THE BEST
Floyd 'Money' Mayweather defeated Big Show by knockout

CAREER THREATENING MATCH
Shawn Michaels defeated Ric Flair

BELFAST BRAWL
JBL defeated Finlay

MONEY IN THE BANK LADDER MATCH
CM Punk wins

SMACKDOWN VS RAW
Batista defeated Umaga

ECW CHAMPIONSHIP MATCH
Kane defeated Chavo Guerrero

BUNNYMANIA LUMBERJACK MATCH
Beth Phoenix & Melina defeated Ashley & Maria